HOT WHEELS™
Race the World!

By Ace Landers & Illustrated by Dave White

SCHOLASTIC INC.

New York Toronto London Auckland

Sydney Mexico City New Delhi Hong Kong

ISBN-10: 0-545-15346-8
ISBN-13: 978-0-545-15346-1

12 11 10 9 8 7 6 5 4 3 2   9 10 11 12 13/0

Printed in the U.S.A.   23
First printing, September 2009

Today an awesome race begins.

Day 1: Peru, South America

The cars will race around the world!

Day 2: Mali, Africa

4

Day 4: Vietnam, Asia

3

Day 3: Antarctica

The first stage of the race
is in the mountains.

Day 1: Peru, South America

The red car kicks up dirt.

The green car cannot see the course. It drives into the trees.

The yellow car makes a fast turn.

It is tied with the red car.

Both cars hit the ramp at the same time.

Which one wins the first race?

The yellow car wins this round.

The second race is in the desert.

Day 2: Mali, Africa

It is hard to drive on the sand.

The purple car jumps over a dune.

The cars are not the only
wild things on this racecourse.

The red car pulls into the lead.

The red car wins the second race!

The third race is in the snow.

This course is dangerous.
The snow is slippery.

The ice
can crack.

Watch out
for penguins!

There can also
be avalanches.

The green car is back in the race!

The green car wins!

The last race is in a forest.

Day 4: Vietnam, Asia

The race is tight!

Which car will win?

We have a Race the World winner!